LIVING ON THE EDGE

by

ALLY LAW

© Copyright Preston Media International Limited (UK) 2020

LIVING ON THE EDGE

Copyright © 2020
Preston Media International Limited

First Published in 2020 (UK)
Printed in the U.K.

Author: Ally Law
Cover Design: Rob Williams
Production: PRESTON

Preston Media International Limited & Alastair "Ally" Law, take
no responsibility nor are liable for any consequences of following any
advice; imitating, or replicating any actions described in this publication. This book should be interpreted as a work of fiction, any
references or similarities to real people are coincidental.
Distribution of this publication without the prior written consent of
the publisher is forbidden.

PREFACE

I have done my best to keep this book to the point. I do my best to give context to my stories or beliefs, and to share my viewpoints on the events discussed.

I want it to be remembered that the beliefs I share are just that: *Beliefs*.

My undeniable online following puts me in a difficult position of being both a role-model, and an entertainer. For the type of content I produce, this contrast of roles often leads me, without intention, to project-upon my audience *my own* beliefs and morals.

In this book, I share my beliefs, but please let it be read as the beliefs of Ally Law. Not of you; not of somebody you respect or look up to, but of somebody whose stories, lessons or viewpoints spark curiosity, excitement or thought. Feel free to agree with me, but do not do so at the expense of your own beliefs and certainly do not make decisions on life (or death) based on the viewpoints or ideas you will read.

For Stan; my Mum;
Granddad, & the millions of
people who have allowed my
dreams to come true.

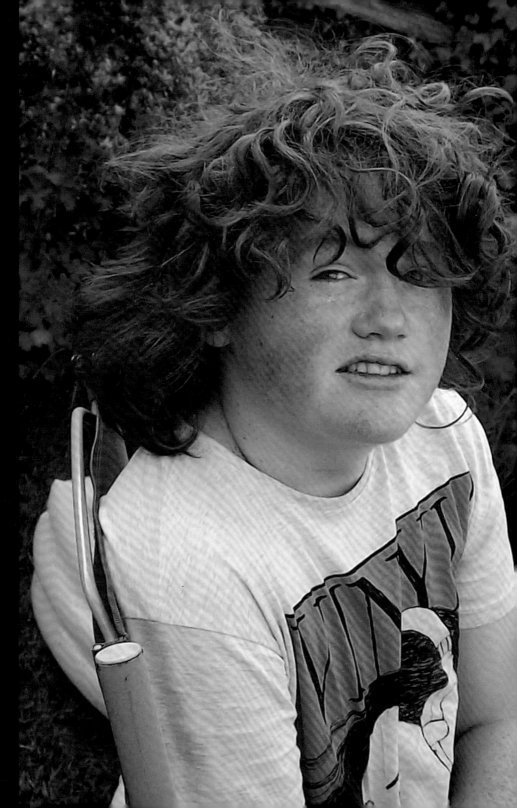

THEFT BY CONSUMPTION

I had arranged in January of 2019 to visit an old friend of mine who lived in Helsinki. For a while at the time, I had wanted to try to tackle a challenge which was completely new to me. I had seen online, people in regions such as the one my friend lived in, cutting holes in the ice, stripping down, and jumping in to the intensely cold water beneath. I've heard many say it was the worst experience of their life, and many say it was intense, but life-changing in a positive sense. Well, my friend in Finland happened to know of a place nearby where I decided I would take-on this challenge for a video, and soon enough, the plane tickets were booked and before long, I was on the road to Gatwick.

During the drive, I didn't think about much, as it was a long drive and I was knackered. The late-night drive reminded me of a video we recorded a year ago, where Ryan and a few others and I snuck into an indoor ski-slope in Milton-Keynes. I remember editing and being proud of how the footage came out, and how much of a bizarrely fun experience that night was. The video was released to relative success. It showed us managing to enter the building in our classic style, messing around on the slopes for several hours – Ryan had even brought his BMX inside!

We'd powered up the lift and enjoyed much of the equipment and what the slopes had to offer during the day when they were open, but after some time had passed, we turned off the lights, had a quick cup of tea in the reception, and left without causing any damage, or leaving anything behind. The video captured our childlike excitement during the whole adventure – and I was proud of it.

Some adventures of ours definitely stuck-out among the rest in my memory, some fade into a blur, but this particular occasion was one memory I often visited.

I arrived at the airport with two of my mates who would be joining me, Fin, and Owen. We checked in and settled down in a terminal seating area only to find out our flight was delayed. However, the delay was only short, so we waited where we were. Looking around the nearby gates, I felt eyes on me. I wrote it up to paranoia from my lack of sleep, but I definitely felt a strange sense of being watched.

Some time passed. Another announcement. Our flight was delayed, but this time, for a lot longer — over two hours! I elected to get some rest. It was a less-busy area of the terminal, so I put my legs up and got some shuteye.

"Boarding will now begin, for Norwegian flight 8371 to Helsinki"

We gathered our luggage and tired brains to the back of the long queue at the gate. We would be last to board.

As we queued, I again felt the same, strange feeling of being watched. I mentioned to Owen, who I'm certain didn't even hear my words, before again resolving to myself that I was sleep-deprived and imagining things, and that I would soon be onboard the plane where I could have some decent rest before our adventure began.

Gatwick airport had recently suffered from a 'Drone-Attack'. Somebody had decided it was a great idea to fly a toy drone around the airport, directly in the landing path of the planes, which, of course, caused widespread delays, as well as a huge investigation and search for the culprit. The day of this incident, I was scrolling through Twitter and saw probably five or six other internet personalities, celebrities, and YouTubers jokingly tweeting along the lines of

"Great fun seeing all the planes land from close-up on my new drone!", and "Wow Gatwick looks great from up here!" followed by a photo from Google Earth of the airport. The response to these was what you'd expect – everyone knew they were a joke, some thought it distasteful, but nothing spectacular. I thought this was great fun – and made my own similar tweet. Soon after, I took a photo of Gatwick from Google Earth on my phone, and shared to my Snapchat story the caption *"New video soon 'Flying a Drone over Gatwick airport' *the army came*"* in satire of YouTube 'click-baiting' titles.

Within minutes, the screenshots of my joke had gone viral. The Sun; The Daily Mail; The Mirror – all major tabloids in the UK and even abroad had rushed out a story. 'Could Ally Law be the Drone Attack Culprit?' Suffice to say, it wasn't me. I wasn't anywhere near Gatwick at the time – and I assumed those responsible for the investigation wrote off my admission as exactly what it was – a poorly-timed joke.

My mind was cast back to that day when I noticed several, rifle-wielding airport police officers stood by the entrance to the bridge from the terminal to the aircraft. I looked down the terminal and saw a similar sight at the nearest few gates. I thought it odd that they were there, I scanned my passport with the attendant at the gate and walked through the open door to the bridge. At the same time, two officers started through the door behind me. I didn't think too much of it, but glanced over my shoulder, to see that two had become five, and five soon turned to over a dozen.

"Shit. What did I do?" My mind was once-again cast back to the Gatwick drone-incident day. Did they think it *was* me?

The taller of the two original police officers, sporting a black and white police baseball cap held my shoulder.

"Fuck. What have I done? I must have really fucked up this time." I said to myself. "This is bad."

"Alastair Law, you are under arrest for burglary"

"Burglary!?" I couldn't for the life of me think what I'd done recently that could constitute an arrest for burglary! I've never stolen, and never knowingly committed a criminal offense.

They led me down some stairs and into a Gatwick police van. My heart raced. Two of the arresting officers came down to talk to me; They stood in front of me.

"We need to talk to you about the drone"

I was relieved to hear them say this, because I knew that I was innocent, and could easily prove to them that it wasn't me. But I had been arrested for burglary? Not terrorism offences, or anything that could define the drone incident. I felt a concerning mix of relief, confusing, and frustration. I said what I've always been told to say in these situations:

"I can't discuss anything without my solicitor"

The relief turned to fear, and the frustration grew as now it had sunk in that my exciting plan to fly to Finland was no more. The officers seemed bored, which felt strange.

"We just need to know if it wasn't you" the other said, with his eyes halfway back in his head.

"It wasn't me."

"OK then."

The two officers left me alone, before two others in strikingly different police uniforms entered the van in the driver and passenger seat.

"Where is it we're going then?" I asked.

"Milton Keynes Station, mate!" One officer responded.

Milton Keynes? Milton Keynes. Shit.

In fairness, the two officers were probably the coolest I've ever interacted with. They didn't seem to know the details of what I was being arrested for, nor did they know who I was, or what I was known for either. They made pleasant conversation with me for the entire drive of almost three hours, discussing my job, lifestyle, as well as various other simple but pleasant conversation.

We arrived and I was tossed into a cell and I did not mind one bit! I was shattered. I slept like a log in that cell in Milton Keynes. Eventually, I was brought in for an interview with a detective. They asked me about the ski-slopes. Why I went there. Who I was with. There was little they could ask me that I would be able to answer without my solicitor, and they knew this. They asked me the normal questions, and I answered what I could honestly, but the conversation was mostly one-sided, with me simply responding with "No comment" I was confident I had not committed any criminal offence, but I was aware the charge was serious.

Later, I had a meeting with my solicitor. He was not as confident. We spent the best part of an hour talking about possible punishments if I were found guilty of Burglary. It was a serious situation, and my confidence shrunk. My awareness faded into a blank stare, as I heard words I didn't want to hear…

"Five to ten years in prison…"

Suddenly I was very present. What did they have on me? As I've said, I've never knowingly committed a criminal offence.

I sat alone in the cell thinking about prison, and the example they were going to make out of me, the infamous boy, 'running amuck' around the UK.

Hours went by. I couldn't sleep anymore. I thought about the ski slopes – and the fun night we had there, and how it may be about to end my career, and change my life forever.

I thought about Owen and Fin going to Finland without me, and how I should have been there jumping into exhilaratingly cold waters, filming videos, and exploring Helsinki.

My fear manifested into sadness, and then back to fear, and then back to sadness again. I felt tenser than I ever felt standing on a one-hundredth floor ledge, one slip from an exhilarating plunge of a different kind.

Eventually, I was allowed out. 'Released pending investigation'. I left the cell and walked dizzily to the reception area, where I was to be handed a charge sheet. My mind raced thinking about what counts would be listed. What would be written on this paper would determine how the rest of my life would play out.

"Alastair Law." The officer behind the screen reaches over and hands me the paper.

Never in my life have I ever, or will I again experience the sheer relief that I did in this exact moment when I read the words on that sheet of paper. The joy was joined by overwhelming hilarity and disbelief.

Charge 1 of 1: Burglary - Theft of a Hot Beverage of Value Unknown.

I was being charged for making a cup of tea! I couldn't' believe it.

The delight I was feeling didn't really wear-off until one thought crossed my mind…

"This is going to go to trial!"

I couldn't fathom the thought of standing in a suit-and-tie in a courtroom, being tried for making a cup of tea! Of course, technically this is the perfect definition of burglary. Through non-criminal means, we illegally entered a premise, and consumed property which wasn't ours – thus "permanently depriving" the owner of their property. I knew this – and had had this explained to me by my solicitor, but something about sitting trial for this crime felt downright bizarre!

Ryan, who was with me on the date of our criminal escapade, had now also been arrested and charged. Ironically, he was getting *off* a plane into Gatwick when he was arrested, having arrived back from a BMX competition in Europe. Our trial date was set. 10th June, Aylesbury Crown Court. *Crown Court.* For those of you who aren't as clued up with the British legal system as those in my line of work are required to be – there are two main court systems to be aware of for now: Magistrates – A judge makes the decision on if you are innocent or guilty, and deals the sentence, usually reserved for Civil Offences, like trespassing, and less serious crimes; and Crown Court — where a *jury* is to decide your fate.

The humor, and my confidence surrounding the entire situation returned. Perhaps it was arrogance, but I have always made it clear with my words, actions, and through my reputation that I never mean to do harm to anyone or anything, and so, facing a trial with a *jury* for stealing a cup of tea, in the context of the entire scenario, was quite frankly, hilarious.

We were informed the Judge in our trial of grandeur, would be a man by the name of Sheridan. I always assumed, growing up, that all judges were, to an extent, clones of one another. But since courts became a sadly more common part of my career, I learned that who the judge in your trial is, is very important. I won't go into detail, because this isn't a legal journal, and I am not a lawyer, or judge, or anyone remotely qualified to go into the intricacies of the legal world. But to you and me, some judges are more lenient, some are less. Some judges are liberal, some have more conservative views. Judge Sheridan was well known for his blunt, and sometimes controversial, personal views on cases and verdicts. We'd been shown a list of recent cases he'd resided over that were somewhat similar to ours, and it didn't look good for us. But this was a jury-led trial, so we didn't need the judge to like us. Not to be found innocent at least!

We arrived at the courthouse, which now was swarming with journalists at the entrance. I imagine they had seen the unusual charges brought against the two of us, and being controversial figures, thought it would make for a good article.

After a day at trial, and a judge whose response to our careers, the crime, and scenario was exactly how we expected it, the Judge removed the charge related to the cup of tea theft, but did add a charge relating to us using the business' electricity unlawfully.

Probably one of the funniest elements of the day at court, wasn't the charge, or rather bland outcome of the proceedings, but the fact that shortly after the trial, whilst Judge Sheridan was yelling at seemingly everybody in the room, a female officer approached me at the prison box.

"This is for you..."

She handed me a blank A5 piece of scrap-paper. I turned it over, to reveal the words:

'My daughter is a big fan. Autograph?'

At this moment, they could have given me the full five-year sentence for that cup of tea, and the smile would have still been on my face.

I thought it was fair enough that we were charged for the electricity usage. Plus, at least we wouldn't see a prison cell. I doubt there would have been many there whose kids are big fans.

IT'S A START

I was born and raised in Southampton, a port-city in the south of England, and from when I was born, my family never had the luxury of disposable income, or much money at all. But we did have love, and lots of it. My whole upbringing, I was surrounded with kindness and love from my whole family. I'm the youngest of three brothers, and always somewhat felt like I was different to them, partially because of the age differences, and partially due to my inability to behave in a way that was deemed sensible. I was always getting in to mischief, and always doing things I was told not to do. I just had a sense of curiosity for everything; always wanting to explore in the small world of my hometown.

From the relatively normal climbing trees, to rolling down hills in wheelie-bins with my friends; playing football, leaping into water from, what I considered to be, great heights. I've always been outdoors-type of mischief maker, right from the start.

I was desperate to learn to ride a bike from the moment I could walk, so much so, that I remember the day I finally was able to get on a bike without stabilisers, at only three years old. At age three, I pulled off the stabilisers from my kids bike, and over, and over, and over again, I picked it up, got on, and fell off. All day. Onto the pavement; Into a bush, or on to my face. I wish I was as cool as I felt I was that day, when I finally was riding my bike outside my house, alongside my much older brothers, when it finally clicked.

Ironically, this memory has a less inspiring ending – I went on to get hit by a car on that same little white bicycle not too long later. I was only a little older, and was riding furiously around the block in my classic youthful fashion, racing my brothers and some friends, as I flew past our imaginary finishing line, represented by a broken wall nearby our family home, a car sped around the corner and crashed into little Ally head-on. I flipped over the bonnet and landed on my head in the centre of the road. The driver got out of his car and rushed around to me. All I remember was thinking about how much trouble I was going to get in, and how big a telling-off this man was about to give me for crashing my bike into his car. Looking back, he was probably far more afraid of the consequences he could be facing. Luckily, I was okay, and spent the next few minutes frantically apologising to the kind man whose car I'd ridden into.

My Mum later told me that the man had won a sizable jackpot on a lottery draw that day, and purchased the sporty vehicle for himself just hours previously! I suppose you could say we were both very lucky that day, as there was little damage, both to me, and the car.

It's not necessarily an impressive memory, but as an adult now, living a lifestyle where I'm constantly trying to learn and evolve new skills, I often think back to my first realisation of one of the rules which I swear-by and try to promote: Do not give up. Confidence will get you what you want. Confidence is a theme throughout this book, and if you know much about me, my brand and my content, then you'll know why.

I loved school — I was a social-butterfly, and loved spending time both indoors and out with my friends, but slowly, as time went on, *family* life at home took a noticeable turn for the worse. For some time, it was a daily occurrence that my Dad would come home drunk. A routine soon developed, and he would regularly shout and smash up our house; police would be called, and a day or so later, it started over again. It wasn't until recently I realised how much this affected me. Whilst all of this was ongoing, thanks to my older brother Cameron, I developed an immeasurable addiction to a computer-game called Runescape, at the height of which, I didn't attend school for almost a full year! My Mum had finally had enough, and when I was around twelve years old, she kicked our Dad out of the house. He left, and moved on, away from his life with us.

I look back on memories of my Dad fondly, despite the last year or so I knew him. I see him as a man who always meant well, and in his character, was a good and fun father to me and my Brothers, but who lost control of a serious problem, for which he probably should have, and hopefully has by now, received proper help for. I hope he is in a better place in his life now – and managed to find the help he needed.

I had never really made the connection until recently between my addiction, and the problems at home. It was an escape for me, and one that I didn't want to part with. It hurt my Mum — I was *her* escape, and my refusal to go to school, locking myself away for hours, really hurt her. I can't image how much I added to her stress during that year, the constant arguments, her asking me what she'd done wrong. I'll never forgive myself for that. I had gained weight, up to about 15½ stone, and now had long, knotted ginger hair, all the way down to my lower-back.

It took me so much time to get out of this rut, well over a year, maybe more than two, until one day I logged into my computer as I always did, only to be 'scammed' out of almost all of my-in-game-currency I had been addicted to earning for the previous eighteen months. I was angry, and sad. I cried a lot, punched my door and kicked my bed for a short while, and then I just sat there, with my PC running, looking down at my legs. I tapped my palms on my thighs; my large, overweight thighs. This was my turning point. I cried more, and grabbed at my legs, realising what I'd let happen to myself, my health; my education, my Mum. I turned off the computer and went into my Mum's room, to tell her I wanted to change, and that I was sorry. I'd gotten my Mum so close to real trouble so many times for my refusal to attend school, we'd had administrators and councillors at the house, we even had to attend court one day. I told her I was sorry. We cried together, and watched TV in her bed. She made me a salad, which I ate, and I never touched Runescape again.

Childhood addiction is far more commonplace that is acceptable to talk about. It doesn't take the form of coming home and wrecking a house in an inebriated rage; or ruining your life betting away every penny you own. For me, it took the form of a desperate escape from the real world; eating my emotions, and letting my addiction take over my feelings and ability to be happy. Maybe addiction is genetic, maybe it's not, I'm not really qualified to say, but in my opinion, it is a little of both.

I missed out a lot on my education as a result, and a lot of growing up, which I'm sure many could tie-in to my current career and lifestyle, but I think that I just never really was able to 'be a teenager', because of the choices I made, and my experiences at such a young age.

After missing these two or so years, I was determined to get back to school. I went on a strict diet, got back my crazed motivation to achieve what I wanted. I was extremely overweight, and was disgusted when I looked in the mirror at how unhealthy and unclean I had become.

Around a week after turning off my PC, I went in to school for the first time in what had felt like forever. I have no idea how I had the confidence to walk back in there, people mistook me for a dangerously overweight young girl! My hair was long and greasy, and I wore clothes that barely fit me.

"Is that Ally?!" I would hear, walking down the corridors.

"Oh my god, is that Ally Law?"

"He got so fat!!"

These were all regular comments I would hear and brush off, as I was now on a mission to get back to who I knew I was underneath. The Ally who would get back onto his bike after falling into the hedges time and again — An active, *confident*, and adventurous child.

I remember going up to my mate Jordan, and hearing his first words said to me in over two years.

"You've got fat; Haven't ya!" He didn't say this in a horrible, or gossipy way, though, the banter was quite a nice way of breaking the ice once again, and addressing the elephant in the room.

My Mum spent £50 on an old exercise bike, which I was to spend an hour on, every day, blaring music from my little gold iPod Shuffle. We would go on walks together regularly, and my diet became infinitely cleaner. My thighs would get sores from chafing, and I could barely walk half a mile before needing a rest - but I powered through, as much for me, as for my Mum, who had become my biggest supporter, a role she adopted and still holds firmly to this day.

Every kilogram I lost would be a self-esteem boost for me, and the growth of my confidence was tangible with every walk I went on, getting less and less overweight as the months went on. It wasn't all easy though — I was bullied quite severely due to my weight, which I expected, and usually didn't let it bug me. But when my self-esteem was lacking, the comments really stuck with me.

I remember going on a school-trip to a nearby Zoo, and stopping en-route at a McDonalds in a service-station. I was counting calories, and so ordered the smallest meal I could get without drawing attention to myself, with a Diet-Coke.

"*Diet* Coke? What's the point!" Two girls from my class sniggered behind me. I was so hurt by this comment, as I felt my efforts over the past year or so were being mocked. *Always* be kind; There is never a reason not to be. We were kids, and I forgive them for it, but please never treat someone like this.

I wish I had more photos of myself at my worst to show you, and to look back on myself. I'm encouraged by my own ability to pull myself out of that dark place at such a young age, and being able to look back on it through a more visual-medium would benefit me a lot, as well as provide for some much-needed visual aid in this chapter.

When I was sixteen, I left school with no idea what I wanted to do with my life. I didn't want to go to college, as my overwhelmingly negative experience in that last year had left me with a sour taste in my mouth. I followed in my Brother's footsteps and took on a Carpentry apprenticeship. I was told it was a good career path for someone without the best education, or professional skills. I'd have good training, a good set-up for life, and a stable career. I'd earn a wage I could live off without too much concern, and maybe be able to go on holiday once a year. Being a sixteen-year-old boy from a council-estate, with no qualifications, that was all I could dream of. I had no role models, nobody told me I could go out and make something for myself; 'success stories' of people from my kind of backgrounds just didn't exist.

I didn't *mind* the carpentry apprenticeship. I made some friends who were mostly from similar backgrounds, with little to no qualifications nor knowledge of what to do with their lives. Some of them poured their hearts into their jobs and the training, others didn't really bother.

For the first twelve weeks I had to spend in the head office of the carpentry business, I was training in. It was a dusty, dark and dingy warehouse, filled with teenagers, without a GCSE between them! We were all in the same boat, and that was okay with me. Everyone had their own story, and I'm a huge advocate that you don't need a qualification to make something of yourself. We had some fun at this warehouse. Being taught the basics, it wasn't particularly interesting, but I was being *paid* for it. This was something I had never experienced before.

The twelve weeks came and went, and it was time for me to move to my first actual building-site. This was when I realised I could not, and would not do this job for the rest of my life. I worked below a man named Alan, who, to this day, was the most miserable man who I have ever met. Everything was a problem to Alan, and if the slightest thing went wrong, he would take great pleasure in screaming in your face. Young or old, he would happily call you a "Useless c—t", if you brought him the 4x4 wood from one palette and not another. This man was the first time I ever had a role-model, and he was a role model for exactly who I did *not* want to end up like.

As time went on, I felt more and more like I was wasting my life. After a miserable two years, I was now setting myself up for sixty more. I wasn't going to waste any more time.

As I mentioned, during my time as an apprentice-carpenter, I made some cool friends, one of them was called Calum. Calum was from nearby, and would tell me about this place just up the road from our site, a 'Free-Running Gym', and after some encouragement from him, I went. I fell in love with this. It was the most amazing thing I'd ever experienced, falling so deeply for an activity until then I'd known nothing about! I would go on to meet so many friends at that gym, spending hours flipping ourselves around and having fun, I loved it. Every friend I have in Southampton now, I met at this gym. Once again, I had become addicted, to exercise and the thrill that parkour gave me. It was a good feeling to lasso my addictive personality and use it to pull me deeper into something positive, helping me make new friends, learn a skill, and get fitter. I would go up to three times a week, and it had officially become my new means of escape.

I owe my life, the way it is now, to Calum, for introducing me to that gym. I strongly believe there is a positive sign in every negative circumstance. If I hadn't have gotten addicted to Runescape, missed out on so much school, and ended up where I did, I wouldn't have gone on to discover my true passion. From miserably working in a building site, with no prospects or future ambitions, to writing a book about my life and lessons so far… I never would have guessed! But, from there on out, I was desperate to make my life all about what I loved — Freerunning, and Parkour.

When I told my Granddad that I was going to start making YouTube videos, after saving for months at my apprenticeship to buy a second-hand GoPro camera, he told me:

"It's better to try and fail, than to always wonder 'what if?'"

My Granddad passed away before ever having the opportunity to see how that leap of faith changed my life, and allowed me to live out my dreams. I made that quote my bio on Twitter that day, and it's been that ever since.

Perhaps, you are somebody who desperately is seeking adventure. Perhaps, you are somebody looking to find, or rekindle an excitement you once felt. I think that everybody wishes they had a bit more excitement in their life.

I make videos on the internet. I film myself and my friends doing the things that the kid in everybody would love to do. We climb; hide; play, and teeter on the edge of the law for the purpose of entertainment and thrill.

I've written this book, with all of its stories, to entertain. I'm not a scholar or field-expert, and I don't intend to preach as if I am, but I want to show through these stories my belief, that with confidence, anything is achievable, and everything can be exciting.

You don't need to stand on the edge of a skyscraper to enjoy life. You don't need to jump off bridges to feel excited – and you certainly do not need to break the law to learn a lesson.

I intend to share with you that rush of adrenaline, and the passionate chasing of thrills, outside the realms of any sane human being's comfort zone, and into that far-away part of our brains, that so desperately desire a grin-inducing, leg-twitching, edge-of-your-seat rush that comes with watching, hearing, or experiencing the type of thrills that I have, and that I've shared with millions of others over the last five years, as well as tell you a bit more about who I am, and why I live life the way I do.

RUN FOR YOUR LIFE

PART ½

There's plenty of risk in my lifestyle, which is why I actively discourage my supporters from following in my footsteps, figuratively and literally!

I've had my fair share of minor injuries, thankfully never anything life-altering, or dramatic. That isn't saying that I'm great at doing what I do. I have trained well, however, I've learned to put a significant focus on reducing complacency as I get more experienced in climbing. Confidence is something I like to promote to my audience, but with confidence and ability, comes complacency, and it is important that the see-saw of confidence to complacency is kept in-check.

Jordan, a good friend of mine who I met at the same free-running gym where I trained and spent so much of my time, was with me, climbing around Southampton. We were putting into practice the things we learned and developed in the safe environment of the gym. Jordan was climbing from a sturdy drainpipe, in an attempt to maneuver up to another friend of ours' balcony, when he slipped and fell several stories. He hit the ground – hard. We'd later learn he had, in-fact, broken almost every bone in his body.

It was a numbing, and shocking event, to know that a friend had fallen and injured himself like that. Somebody who I deemed to be as, or if not *more* skilled than I was, hurt himself so seriously, really put me off climbing for some time. It's not something you easily move past. Of course, it must have been infinitely worse for Jordan! It made me focus on the idea of confidence verses complacency, to the point where I now very intricately plan everything I do. I evaluate the risk involved, and the most likely points of danger. I have Jordan to thank for that, who later made a full recovery after a significant time in hospital.

I only have two experiences to date where I've genuinely feared for my safety. Both of which were as a result of my reputation preceding me. Most of the time people know that we never cause damage or steal, but occasionally, we cross the wrong people.

In late 2018, some friends, Alex, Owen, Scotty, Harry, and I, had decided to attempt to climb to the roof of Liverpool football club's home stadium, Anfield. We were loaded into my van and made the journey north from Southampton. We arrived late into the evening – Owen, Alex and I wanted to get started right away, whilst Scotty and Harry decided to stay in the van and sleep.

Football stadiums, despite often being a bit of a mashup of various metal and brick structures, are fairly difficult to gain access to. We circled the perimeter, and eventually had found our route to the roof… We were to scale a set of vertical steel beams to the first roof, where we would come up with a further plan in order to make it to the very top of the stadium's highest point. Let me tell you, this climb was sketchy! Not only was it tall and difficult to climb, but it finished with a two-meter wide leap to safety. The jump was at least fifteen meters in the air, from what was essentially a cold, steel trestle, to the roof.

Once we were all safely up, we discussed our options for getting to the top of the main grandstand roof, although now that we could view it from a different perspective, it was clear we wouldn't be able to make it from where we currently were. We scaled into the inside of the stadium, and made our way through the labyrinth of stand sections and plastic seating to the pitch. Upon a further discussion, we decided our best course of action was to head to the opposite side of the stadium, to the base of the main stands, where we would begin our ascent.

We were inside one of the many access corridors when we were confronted by security. The three of us have had our fair share of apprehension by security workers, sometimes they're rougher than others, and it was clear this was one of those times. From the start, we were pushed and tugged around like ragdolls. Our two captors were a lanky gentleman we'll call Tim, and a second, considerably more overweight, bald guard whom we'll call Tom.

Tim and Tom grab us by the arms and drag us to a nearby lift, in which we descend to a basement level. Soon, we're dragged out once again into a very unnerving, concrete storage room. In situations like this where we are being treated particularly roughly, without opportunity for explanation, it has become second nature to me to glance around the room for any security-cameras. My eyes darted left and right.

"Cameras. Phew." I felt relived, knowing that we would never be hurt or held for long when we were in full view of security feeds, which could only be used against any overly-brutal guards in court.

A third guard was waiting for us, and Tim and Tom stepped aside. The third guard was somehow even larger than Tom, and although clearly angry, he had a somewhat pleased demeanor about him.

"Hello Ally."

He separated me from the others and physically dragged me to the end of the room and through a doorway into another, smaller, concrete room. My eyes darted once again… No cameras.

I was naturally resisting being dragged into this room by a man who was giving off incredibly sinister vibes. I was being held on the floor as he picked up his phone and made a call. He didn't use many words in the short conversation he had, but he was mad. My gut said that this was bad – Really bad. These people seemed serious, and *seriously* angry.

"He's here… Yes. Of course. Yes, It's him. My pleasure"

He smiled an eerie smile and looked down on me. It definitely was not the police on the other end of the line, I could tell by the way he spoke and hung up without any pleasantries or exchanging of information. He didn't say where we were; who he was, or what had happened. He knew this person – and this person knew me.

My heart moved up my throat more and more, as I demanded answers and from him and explained that we weren't here to cause harm. I was certain that this would be ending with a beating for me, or worse, as opposed to the usual yelling and wrist-slap we were used to.

I look up and see one of the original two guards, Tom, enter the concrete room that had been made my prison, and potentially soon-to-be torture chamber…

They exchanged one or two words which I didn't catch, but it was clear that the guard who took the phone call was in charge.

Tom's voice was raised slightly above his senior's, allowing me to hear his demanding plea for my captor to not do whatever he may have just been about to.

"Call the police... Absolutely not... No-no-no! Call the police mate.... Do the right thing."

The guard in charge's smile had vanished, his eyes rolled back in his head and his fists clenched. Soon after, the police were called. Two officers arrived, both middle-aged men, one was holding a very disinterested German shepherd dog on a lead, the other was a taller man in a trench-coat, which was very odd for police, and a sight I had never seen before.

They took us out to their van parked nearby and sat us in the back. The officer with the dog watched over us. Trench-Coat slams the front door and starts back towards the stadium.

"Stay there." He said angrily to the dog-handling officer, who was, in fact, already *staying there*. Trench-coat was not there to fuck-around, and was taking the situation incredible seriously – more so than his disinterested colleague:

"You won't get arrested." He chuckles to us. "We know exactly who you are."

His pleasant and jokey demeanor gave us some comfort. It turned out he was somewhat of a fan of the videos. We chatted briefly about our adventures, and this particular event, in between reassurances from him that we won't be arrested for this, and it will all just disappear.

Trench-coat reappears. He retrieves a pair of handcuffs and swiftly turns me around, securing my wrists tightly.

"Alastair Law, you are under arrest for criminal damage."

I was stunned! So, it seemed, was officer fan-boy, who backed away out of our view, clearly quite embarrassed.

We were taken to the police station and separated once again. Officers moved me from room to room, until eventually I was moved to a grey room with a table and four chairs at the side by the wall. For hours on end, I was interrogated as if I was Pablo Escobar, or the leader of a terrorist cell. Questions moved focus from me to my Van. They knew I had it with me, as its keys were seized with me upon my arrest, and they were desperate to know where it was.

I very rarely, if ever, will answer questions without my solicitor…who wasn't there. That didn't stop the endless attempts for the location of my van from rolling in. Hours went by at the station. The interviewing officer now informed me that Harry and Scott, who stayed behind in the van when the adventure began, had been arrested, and my van seized. They were certain that the two of them had been inside of the stadium with us, which of course, they hadn't been.

I was interviewed a few more times over the next twenty-four hours by various individuals and branches of the police. In an interview with the Criminal Investigation Division, or CID, I was treated especially seriously. They kept asking me how much I was paid for my 'hits'… Who was it that 'recruited me', and so on.

From these bizarre interviews, and discussion with my solicitor, it was clear that they were trying to create a charge for a criminal case, where there was not one.

People disagree with what I do — that is both fair, and understandable. This chapter isn't about my reasoning, but I want to make clear that in my opinion, if you genuinely commit a crime, it is fair and just to be charged and tried as appropriate. However, if a crime has not been committed, then trying to 'throw the book' at them simply to make an example, is inherently unjust. Then again, I'm just a nutty building-climbing school dropout, so what do I know! Liverpool Football Club and the stadium owners will clearly pursue a *civil case*, which they are well within their rights to do, but I have done no damage, committed no crime, and acted peacefully throughout. Nonetheless, they wanted to throw the book at me... and boy did they try!

They tried charging me for criminal damage... But there was no damage. They tried charging me under the vagrancy act... an ancient law used to prosecute rough-sleepers in the nineteenth century... That didn't stick either. I was informed in one of the later interviews of my stay in the station, that a bomb search had to be carried out at the stadium, as a result, they attempted a charge of Aggravated Trespassing, which again, disappeared almost as quickly as it was raised.

So, I was let go. After a full twenty-four hours in the cell, the legal maximum without charge, they kicked me out the door, but with no clue as to where my van was. It, with my keys had been seized the night before when Harry and Scott were arrested. I waited for Alex and Owen's release. Nobody knew anything about my van.

Alex retrieved his possessions, but was missing his wallet. After some digging by the administrative officers, it was realized that his wallet, holding his bank-cards, cash, *and* ID, had been mistakenly given to another released inmate. I can't put words on paper to describe how furious Alex, and we all were at this.

With little money, and one fewer wallet than before, we left to stay at a nearby friend's house, whilst we tracked down the van. It took an entire week of discussion with the police to find where our van was being kept. It had seemingly been lost by the police, which in combination with Alex's wallet being given away, felt very dodgy. On the eighth day, we went to collect the van. The impound-lot charged me £400 for its retrieval, citing "Improper Insurance". I definitely had 'proper' insurance. When I asked about this, they said I can claim it back later with proof of the insurance, but after I paid, I never saw that £400 again.

This story is weird start to finish. It began with fearing for my life at the hands of a rogue security officer at Anfield Stadium, and ended with so much police conspiracy. It's hard to ignore. I never got any paperwork that my van was seized, except a memo in the back that had been searched the day before. None of our cameras, laptops or equipment were in there, and it would be another two weeks before we could request to have it back.

As we drove out the impound, I get a call from my insurer, telling me that they were cancelling my policy as a result of my "undisclosed criminal history", which at the time, was non-existent! They listed all the really serious crimes that I have never once been involved in, let alone charged for, that the police had informed them about. Now I needed new insurance, before we could drive away and leave this nightmare behind us!

After sorting out a policy, we finally started to drive. We originally were planning to head to Scotland for some more climbing, but as I'm sure you can tell from the tone, we were all a bit miserable, and ready to go home. We got less than a mile down the road, and my brand-new van began to rattle, and not subtly. Soon, an awful burning smell joined the aggressive shaking. But as if by magic, there was a repair garage nearby, so we rattled our way in.

To our, and the mechanic's surprise, the water-tank cap had been super-glued shut! – So much so, to remove it, he had to drill a hole in the side. My brand-new van had been sabotaged! We were miserable, shocked, and needed to get home. The tank had to be topped-up with water every fifteen minutes of driving or so, but despite our efforts, the van broke down halfway to Blackpool, and we were towed the rest of the way to Southampton.

I never did get any paperwork about my van being seized, nor about our lost items. The whole situation stank of dodgy-dealings on the side of the police, who for the most part, I never have problems with their professionalism.

This, and a few other infamous events, are why I am banned from most football stadiums nationwide, which is fair enough – we did cause a bomb-alert after all… At least that's what they say!

RUN FOR YOUR LIFE

PART 2/2

I was climbing an unfurnished concrete stairwell past the 60th floor, whilst my friends, Alex and Usama, had already turned around to head back to ground level in order to grab some shots of us at the top of the developing skyscraper. We were in Manchester, spending some time in the city doing some exploration and climbing in the growing city's urban districts.

Being based in Southampton, when I started climbing, the majority of what I did was local. Only after a little while did my immediate circle and I, decide that we had 'completed' the city, and so we moved on initially to London, where we achieved some of our most infamous and widely known explorations, and most funny memories.

I remember being turned away from a Nando's restaurant, on account of being banned from the O2 stadium of which it was a part of, after climbing to the roof to watch the sunrise. They let me stay briefly though, enough time to wolf-down my food and immediately leave. It didn't stop us going back to watch the sunrise once more, a few weeks later, however.

We explored London and all it had to offer for quite some time, before again, I felt like I had done all I could, or wanted, to do in the city. London became repetitive and a bit boring. It wasn't until a little while later I, and a few others, decided to go to Manchester, where all of a sudden, it felt like we had discovered a whole new world to explore. I've held Manchester in a special place in my heart stemming from that feeling of delight and excitement about arriving at the city.

We'd stopped our climb up the stairwell and looked out over the lit-up skyline of Manchester, and before long, we could see Alex and Usama exiting hundreds of feet below us. The three of us remaining, Rikke, Adam, and I, decided to wait for a moment and take in the view some more, before continuing the climb for the purpose of the incredible shot we were anticipating from the pair who had returned to the surface. Seeing the lights of a city from near the top of a building is one of my favorite things about what I do. To look out at the hustle and bustle of the night-life in a city; the cars whizzing by – each and every one on their own journey, home or elsewhere – It feels incredibly loud, but from such a height, absolutely silent.

The clouds glowed with the reflection from the beaming moon; The tip of each building accented with a red bead of light, and the darkness of the empty office buildings. On the road, cars; bikes, and dozens of flashing blue lights heading straight in our direction—

"Shit – Are those for us?!"

From our viewpoint, we anxiously watch them approach the building from directly ahead of us, whilst Alex and Usama, immediately realizing their arrival, turned around and began running back in the direction of the building site. Emerging from the ground floor of the site was a team of security guards dressed in all-black, who approached the large team of police officers. They conversed whilst taking moments to glance up directly at our floor, and the edge of the scaffold where we stood. We made no effort to evade their glances, as it had become clear that they knew we were there.

Soon, the police turned around, got in their cars and left. Leaving the team of security guards menacingly, but helplessly watching us from far below. They re-entered the building. Almost instantaneously we noticed the echoes of footsteps running up the bare concrete stair-well, and so we start downwards, swapping stairwells every two floors in an attempt to evade, or even confuse our pursuers, and at first, it was seeming to work.

The fiftieth floor became the fortieth; the fortieth became the thirtieth. But the menacing echoes of the guards suddenly started to feel closer and closer. No matter how often we swapped between stairwells, it didn't matter. They had enough people to cover every exit. The echoes grew louder, and we decided it was time to hide. Rikke, Adam, and I hide behind a large pile of pallets on the unfurnished floor. A few moments passed until –

"BOOM!"

The stairwell door slammed open ferociously, revealing the most gigantic human-being you could imagine. If you're able to visualize The Incredible Hulk, combined with a thunder-cloud, that is what this guard looked like. We'll name him Sean. Sean is *not* a happy thunder-cloud! He furiously paces the floor, less than six feet away from our hiding spot, screaming down his radio for more security guards to come and join the search. I wasn't sure what could be more frightening than the thought of Sean beating us to a pulp in a building site, until we were faced with the thought of *ten* Sean's beating us to a pulp in a building site!

We were waiting for what felt like forever, but realistically was less than a few minutes, before he spotted us. Sean puts away his radio and stomps his way over to us. He grabs the three of us simultaneously and drags us along the dusty concrete, our legs practically off the ground.

He throws us, three eighty-something kilogram men, firmly to the ground in the stairwell, like a discarded cigarette butt.

Muscle memory kicks in. My eyes dart. No Cameras.

We're lying against the stairs – Sean leans over us one by one.

"I'm going to kill you! I'm going to kill you! Pull up your sleeves!" He booms in Rikke's face.

"This is the day we get beaten." I remember thinking to myself, over and over again, as he continued screaming at the others.

"Pull up your sleeves. If you have tats, I swear to God—

Adam and Rikke frantically roll up their sleeves as Sean pulls out a black police-baton and smashes it into the ground, whilst repeating similar rhetoric.

He seemed to be looking for someone, the tattoos being their identifying mark. I didn't have tattoos, but this didn't ease my nerves, or calm the terror that had swollen in my skull, or the red-hot adrenaline from Sean screaming and spitting in my face from numbing my skin.

"Trust me, I will smash your kneecaps if you have a tattoo on your arm!"

Still laying against the ice-cold steps, I rolled up my sleeves, and suddenly, Sean's demeanor somewhat restored, like the Hulk shrinking back to Bruce Banner, he had become fully calm. His baton put away, and his voice fell to a normal volume.

Immediately, and in his new friendly demeanor, Sean offered an explanation. He explained to us that another climber had been on a similar site recently, and it had cost his security firm a contract on that site.

"Shit." For the first time, we knew of a significant human impact of one of our adventures. I suddenly felt like the bad guy in the story of this nice man's life... at least, for a few hours...

"I'm a fair man so I'll offer some warning" Sean continues. "If you enter one of our sites again, I *will* kill you."

I felt a little less sorry for Sean now, especially as directly after this threat, he took photos of all of our IDs, and noted our addresses.

"Don't think I won't pay you a visit."

As it turns out, from a small amount of research, Sean's company happened to be significantly linked to a vast array of violent crime in Manchester, mostly gang-related.

You might be wondering if I ever considered going back to any of these sites? The answer to that would be a strong and resounding 'no'.

But as I mentioned, I like Manchester, and frequently visit now. On one occasion, we a few different lads were walking along the pavement in the city center, when three blacked-out Range Rovers pull up alongside us, the window rolled down halfway, to reveal Sean in the back seat.

"Ally." He calls out – "You aren't here climbing my sites are you…?"

"Absolutely fucking not."

BIZARRE DOWN-UNDER

When my online following began to grow, and I was gathering more and more attention and fans every day, I suddenly had something which I wasn't quite used to having: Disposable income. Working in carpentry as my first and only full-time job, I earned absolutely peanuts! If I wanted something, or to go somewhere, it would take me months of saving my income, and I'm not referring to large purchases, like holidays to the Caribbean or a new flat-screen TV, I'm talking about a computer game, or a cheap camera. For the first time, I now had enough money where I could make some significant purchases, both for the good of my content, and for my personal enjoyment.

I'd only really been abroad once before my channel began to grow. Back in 2015, parkour and free-running were still in their very early days of popularity. These were the days where you could go onto Facebook, search "Southampton Freerunning" or "London Freerunning", and find a small group of like-minded hobbyists to meet up with or share spots with. My good friends Ben, Ryan, and

I were travelling around the UK by train, liaising with various people through Facebook about where was best to go to run, or climb. We were in Guildford, and Ben knew of a guy there called Rikke, who we would meet up with for some exploring. We were on a train in Guildford talking about how he and a few others would soon be headed to Denmark for some more of the same. We'd all gotten on quite well that day, and so made the decision to join them on their trip to Copenhagen on that same train journey. We booked the cheapest flights we could find, and soon would head off to explore another country.

That trip still holds its place in my mind, as one of the most fun trips I've been on, simply down to the excitement of leaving the country to do what I love, for the first time.

But now, for the first time, I had some *real* money available to me to go and explore like I'd always dreamed of doing…

It was early 2017, and I was making my way across Australia, getting lifts from whoever I could until I reached each destination. I was in Sydney in the baking Australian summer sun, early 2017, desperate to reach Melbourne for some more exploring. In hindsight, hitchhiking was an incredibly dangerous method of making my away across the country, but I was riding the high of my euphoric traveling experience over the last few months, and was naïve enough to think the classic: Nothing bad will happen to me!

Luckily, on this occasion, I was correct. I actually had a blast meeting such a variety of generous and fun individuals, hearing their stories, woes and joys. Strangers often would disclose more than they might to someone they know, which I always felt formed a sort of bond between two people. One man in particular stuck in my mind, but not for his stimulating conversation, his stories or his generosity. I was waiting at the side of the Hume Highway, having been dropped off once or twice along my route by various others, awaiting my next generous offer of safe passage with a kind stranger. After some time stood around, a ginger in the baking sun, a car pulled over. A man leans over the passenger seat. He had a chiseled jaw, and an intense but friendly look in his eye.

"You're a fucking idiot you know?" His voice raised above the noise from the traffic.

I was confused, and assumed he was joking, but he maintained a calm yet serious demeanor as he further ranted to me about my stupidity for hitchhiking on the Hume Highway. My confusion only grew, but my desire to get out of the sun and on my way to Melbourne outweighed any doubts or concerns I had about getting in the car with this man.

"Haven't you ever heard of Milat?!" He asks.

"Who?" I stepped back from the window, realizing he wasn't quite done with this pre-journey conversation.

"Ivan Milat!?" He goes on, explaining about an apparently very infamous Australian serial killer, who would drive up and down the Hume Highway, kidnapping and keeping prisoner, any hitchhikers he could find, before murdering them in his captivity.

At this point, I'm a bit concerned that this man is just wasting my time. As I'm about to tell him to drive-on, he finishes his rant.

"Get in then. Don't you try anything though. If you do, I've got this." He holds up a six-inch, rusty screwdriver he pulled from his glove-box. This time with a smirk on his face, which put my mind more at ease that his intimidation had been nothing more than a bit of horseplay.

I got in. We set off. The driver told me his name, which I no longer remember, so I'll call him Mike — He probably would disapprove of this story being told with his true identity anyway. He tells me more and more about the details about Ivan Milat, the *'backpack killer'*, and where he used to take his victims, how he was eventually found and captured by the Australian authorities. He seemed to know a lot about this heinous murderer, and although his stories were intriguing, I could not stop thinking about my aching feet, and the unusual vibe this man was giving off!

"You know—" He turned his head to look at me, my head down and looking at the floor, wondering if it would be inappropriate to remove my shoes and let me feet relax freely. "I was Ivan Milat."

"What?" I waited for the punchline. Surely this was another light-hearted joke.

"Yep." He responded. "I played him in the movie."

My confusion returned tenfold - I was stunned. Before I could utter a response, he continued.

"On TV. Couple years ago now, about the whole thing. The murders and catching me." It was odd how he referred to Milat as *'Me'*. I now was looking forward to our journey's end. It's rare that a driver picking up a hitchhiker will be heading in the exact same direction for their entire journey, so it's not unusual that I'd be dropped off a short while after I'd been collected. The conversation continued, and Mike revealed his destination: Melbourne. Shit.

I couldn't deny that it was incredibly convenient to me that I was picked up by someone going to the exact same destination, but this guy was giving off unsettling vibes. Mike continued to drive, as I tried to relax, which was challenging, as Mike's driving was aggressive at best, and terrifying at worst! What really shook me though wasn't his driving ability, every few minutes he'd lift up a Jack Daniel's bottle from the foot-well, swiftly swig from it, and replace it back on the floor. The whole time all I could think was that it had to be some strange prank, and it was in fact cola or something else inside the glass bottle — I still hope this is the case. However, when another driver pulled in front of him, his undeniable road-rage led me to one clear assumption of the contents of that bottle. Mike and I never strayed more than a couple of meters behind that poor driver, honking and cursing, I laughed out of terror and confusion about the situation I'd gotten myself into, until I hear a siren: A police car behind us, instructing us to pull over. Mike slaps his steering wheel with the same vigor as he extended to the driver who he had been tailgating moments earlier. Mike was clearly not in sound of mind to be driving, and the officer would now surely see that, and I could wait for another, more stable, character to continue to my destination alongside.

The police officer came to the driver-side window. Mike rolled it down, and without missing a beat, in a calm and unmistakably sober demeanor, he asks:

"Everything okay officer?"

I tell you, this man deserved an Oscar for his performance, and the policeman bought it. They chatted calmly about the importance of spacing between vehicles, shared a chuckle, and before a moment had passed, the window came up, the officer left, and Mike drove away. My chance at escaping this somewhat dangerous situation had gone, and I was stuck with the drunken Actor, swearing at every pothole.

After several hours on the edge of my seat, we arrived at a small residential area in Melbourne.

"Need to grab my valium. I won't be two ticks" He told me, shortly before bringing the car to a stop outside a smaller, run-down-looking house. He got out and knocked on the door. It opened, he looked left and right, and went inside. Now was my chance. I opened the passenger door and walked around the other side to grab my bag, my legs were tingling from sitting down for so long. I opened the door, took my pack and started off in the direction that felt natural.

I had been walking for a few minutes when Mike's car caught up with me, with Mike leaning out of the window to talk to me. I tell him that I'm okay walking from here, but he insisted he finish the journey of getting me to the city centre; so reluctantly, I got in. However stupid a decision it may have been, thankfully I arrived in one piece.

The early days.

On-site as an apprentice carpenter.

First one-hundred-thousand subscribers.

Backpacking in Australia.

ALWAYS WATCHING

As is quite commonly known, I've had my fair share of trouble from being somewhere that I shouldn't have been. In 2017, I successfully climbed the famous UK theme-park, Thorpe Park's tallest coaster, *'Stealth'*, in the middle of the night which landed me in the public eye for one of the first times: Being taken to court by the company and subsequently banned for life from all of their parks around the world. However, this doesn't compare to the amount of coverage I received for making a special-appearance on the famous Big Brother set during the live show.

I've been putting off writing about this experience, not just because I have to be careful with what I say, but also because it was such an infamous experience, that I was not allowed to share in video-form much to many who knew the story's disappointment, that it is important to me to do it justice!

Ryan and I decided to attempt to make it onto the set of Big Brother during the live-evictions and make it onto television across the UK. For those of you who don't know the concept of Big Brother, the show revolves around a 'House', which is essentially a big enclosed film-set, where a selection of celebrity contestants must live together, without leaving, surviving vote-offs called 'evictions', until there is only one left standing. I never found the show particularly interesting, neither in concept or to watch... But we made it our mission to get on TV!

Attempt one. We arrived at the studios just outside of London where the show is taped, pacing around the perimeter looking for the perfect way in. When we thought we'd found the perfect opening to get us to where we needed to be, we realised we had only got one layer in to the maze of this film set. Ryan and I stood in a messy fenced courtyard with various construction equipment, forklifts and such, all around, and a gate leading into what appeared to be the main backlot. It was dark and incredibly tense. We knew that whoever would potentially find us would not be happy, and that these people would be just over this small gate. We needed a plan, because two young men walking across a major film-studio's backlot in the dead of night reeks of suspicion, and that's if they didn't immediately recognise who we are — after all, our pictures were on almost every cork-board in every security office in the country by this point in 2018.

We walked around the immediate area, looking for a clear path, or a plan to pop into our minds. Well, let me tell you, if there is a 'God of Madnesses', he was looking upon us that day, because, lying across a tractor parked in the darkness, were two high-visibility, orange security jackets. Ryan and I looked at each other with the biggest grins upon our faces. As I always say, with confidence and a high-viz jacket, you can get away with just about anything. We put them on, feeling like we were slipping into cloaks of invisibility, and hopped the gate.

Our feet had barely landed on the floor of the studio's backlot, when we were confronted by a security guard, wearing the exact same jacket we were wearing. He seemed like he was about to fall asleep, and half-heartedly asked us what we were doing. Ryan stayed quiet, and I spoke to him. I don't even remember the words I used, but there were not many. It was an easy blag, and we walked off, increasingly fast as we ducked behind a life-sized street in the middle of the dense studio area.

Ryan pointed out the bright spotlights shining into the sky, barely one-hundred meters from our location.

"No way it's going to be this easy" I thought to myself, as we walked calmly around the alley to the side of the building. We were climbing up scaffolding to the roof, from which we entered one of the 'backstage' sections, behind the mirrors of the set.

We stood there, behind the one-way glass, looking into the celebrity house. At this point, we were beyond excited. I thought that we might actually have pulled it off! Before we continued, Ryan took out his phone and snapped a quick clip through a gap, into the main room, where all the celebrities were waiting for the live eviction to begin!

This was the fatal error in our seemingly flawless plan. Wanting to share our excitement and disbelief, Ryan put the clip onto his public Snapchat story, meaning anyone of his followers, fans, and worst of all, enemies, could see.

An official-looking lady approached us calmly.

"Can I see your credentials please?" she asked politely, but with a distinct sense of suspicion.

"Oh, we left them upstairs!" Ryan and I said as we looked at each other, with a pretending confusion about us, as to why this staff member, was asking *us* for *our* credentials. It seemed to work though, we backed away, and headed the way we came.

We climbed up into a wooden crawlspace, hanging above the Big Brother house, attempting to find a way in.

Within minutes, we could hear activity nearby. Activity on the route we had taken to our hiding spot. Orders being barked and footsteps. We knew it was only a matter of time before we were found, so we pressed on.

Soon enough, a man in a suit jacket soon appeared, and took Ryan by the wrist, and myself by the neck, and before long, we'd been escorted out of the set. We were moved around by security and police officers, whom had now arrived, and eventually, we were presented with an opportunity. Having been moved from cabin to cabin, we found ourselves walking down a fenced alleyway. We darted through the gate and made a run for it. Despite our escape, we felt immensely disappointed. We had made it so far; had so much luck, and within a few minutes, our plans had crumbled. An overwhelming sense of defeat had deflated the excitement of the evening.

"Nope" I told myself, and turned to Ryan, "We're going to do it. We aren't going to take an 'L' on this" I smiled.

I felt a similar kind of determination to our Thorpe Park experience some time ago. A few months before I scaled their roller coaster, we had gained access to the park, but been stopped in our tracks by security having fallen in, and waded through, a swampy river…

When I was a kid, I also visited Thorpe Park with some friends. A day which stuck in my head through all the years. As we all made our way around the park, queuing for all of the rides, I could never join-in with my mates. I would freeze with fear at the thought of getting on any of the rides, let alone the tallest and most intense ride in the park. I have a distinct memory of standing in the shadow of Stealth's two-hundred-foot-tall top-hat, and feeling sick to my stomach.

...We returned to Thorpe Park to make another attempt, using the same entry method. After dodging the masses of security in jeeps with bright lights, there I stood, at the top of the same roller-coaster I felt too scared to ride many years prior. I felt an overwhelming sense of pride in that moment.

Leaving the park that morning of the initial attempt filled me with the same determination as I now felt having been removed from the television studio.

The newspapers had already got ahold of the story of the infamous Ally Law and Ryan Taylor 'breaking in' to the Big Brother Studios, complete with Ryan's Snapchat photo on the front cover of two notable British Tabloids, as well as various international web news sites and blogs. Nonetheless, we knew we would return - and we did.

One week after, on the next scheduled live-eviction, we arrived at the studio. Immediately, we headed to the very same entry point as before. We entered the courtyard. Past the tractor. Over the gate. Past the fake-street. It was all going like clockwork... Until we hear security. Screaming, and running towards us from all directions. We could see the same spotlights shining into the sky and we sprinted as fast as we could towards the building.

We approached the scaffolding at the side of the House's building. Scrambling up, the furious security was hot on our heels. Screams echoed upwards as we rapidly scaled to the roof. We made it up onto a corrugated iron roof. Four long roofs arranged as a square, above the section with the live audience and presenter stood, ready for the evictions to take place. Here, we were untouchable. But we didn't want to be here. We ran across the roof, looking down at the audience, who cheered and shouted as we appeared in their view above the events below. This is where the famous photo used in so many papers was taken.

We needed to find a way into the house if we wanted to complete our mission of getting on TV. We clambered up onto an adjacent metal roof, which sloped down to form another small courtyard, with grass, faux garden fences, and a hot tub in the center, this was obviously the garden of the house!

"Yeah baby!" I shouted with delight, when we finally could see our entrance: Next to a series of large windows, a bright orange door leading into the Big Brother House!

It was a fairly large drop, and my mind was cast back to my friend Jordan, who suffered the nasty fall some years previously. I considered the risk, and my technique, and leapt to the floor of the Big Brother garden. Ryan followed, and jumped a few moments later.

We darted to the door. Furiously shaking the handle up and down in attempt to gain access. It was evident that when the security who had, until moments ago, been hot on our tail, noticed we were back, they triggered a 'lockdown' protocol of sorts. My immeasurable excitement for being where we were right now, though, took-over from any possible disappointment from our now trapped state, outside of the end-goal.

Ryan was laughing endlessly, taking videos through the large windows of the inside of the house. This was our one and only appearance on live TV — If you look *very* carefully, in the background, you can see Ryan and I in the windows behind the celebrities.

The security guards knew where we were now, and had rapidly made their way to the inside of the studio. We backed away from the doors, waiting for them to bust through. The handle shook. They were stuck *in!* Our laughter continued uncontrollably, as we, like schoolchildren, pulled silly faces through the window on the door in response to the muffled screams of the security officers on the other side. We knew soon they would get through though. I had one thing left to do.

"If we're going to get arrested, Ryan, I am getting in that hot tub." I resolved assertively.

I stripped down to my underwear and jumped into the hot tub, the door to the house busting-open as my shoulders went under the warm water.

Shouts echoed around the small grass courtyard. Ryan was desperately scrambling to make it up the wall, back to the safety of the roof. Giving up, he dodged and weaved his way around the security guards now flooding in to our garden-prison. I counted ten or eleven individual guards, dressed in black. Ryan confidently sprinted around on the grass, somehow evading capture, as I sat in the very middle of the hot-tub laughing my arse off!

"Go on, Ryan!" I screamed, in between my bouts of hysteric laughter, with guards now surrounding my hot-tub-prison! He ran around the hot tub, with a grin on his face, spinning and avoiding all of the guards as he did so.

I was chilling-out in the water, furious guards all around me, just laughing at Ryan like I was in the audience of a pantomime... Until my laughter abruptly stopped when an arm threw itself around my neck and dragged me to the edge of the small pool. A security officer screamed into my face with her arm around my neck, dragging me in my underwear out of the hot tub. I had tears rolling down my face from the humor of the entire situation.

We assumed from our treatment this time that the security firm got a massive telling-off for allowing our last attempt to get as far as it did. After several minutes evading capture, Ryan and I lay with knees on our necks and arms, being choked and roughed around by the security agents, before they took us, once again, to meet the police, outside the set of the house.

The rest of this story is history really. As many know, we were convicted of aggravated trespassing for this, having caused no damage, and done nothing but cause inconvenience.

As we stood in court, the evidence being presented by the prosecution, watching my never to be released footage of the whole event, there wasn't a single individual in that courtroom without a smirk or a smile on their face —The judge; the lawyers, everybody.

I felt like my job was done. We had entertained, even though we would be forbidden from uploading our footage by the courts, we had made people smile.

I like to think that we often inadvertently help businesses with their security by doing what we do. We expose flaws in their security, but without the malicious intent. We never, ever intend to cause harm or damage; we haven't always been successful with that, as the court cases have demonstrated, but we do our very best to make clear we don't mean harm.

The Big Brother studios now, no doubt, are better pre-pared for break-ins of a malicious nature, thanks to our harmless stunt; and with regards to Thorpe Park. Al-though the same theory applies, I think that I would say I, to an extent, regret my various madnesses at their compa-ny's network of attractions, as being banned from nearly every major attraction in the UK. A large amount of them across the world is a bit of crap. If anyone at Merlin reads this, I would love to come back to stand in line; go on the rides, like a normal person, once again, at some point in the future.

NUISANCE

I've pissed a lot of people off. It's not something I'm proud of, or happy to have done, especially in cases where I feel genuinely misunderstood, or even just where I don't know what it is I have actually done.

Security guards, site-owners, and other people who I can understand and somewhat relate to their frustration with me become understandably annoyed when we take advantage of exploits or flaws in their premises. I've mentioned previously about nearly having my kneecaps busted, or face beaten-in by enraged, and sometimes rogue, security guards, but there have been cases where I've felt far more afraid, from far less dramatic scenarios.

I've never actively protected my address or where I've lived for most of my internet-career. I do not encourage people coming to my home. It's quite intrusive to say the least, especially as one's following grows, the amount of people who want to come and meet me does too, which isn't always pleasant for me or my family – So, please don't turn up at my house without an invitation! With that said, in the earlier days when my following was mostly local, lots of younger fans would rock-up at my door to say "Hi", usually with their parents. Because it wasn't something I was used to at the time, I didn't particularly mind it. It was humbling seeing teens and young-adults thanking me for not always just entertaining them, but often for pulling them out of dark places with my online silliness; or helping them grow their confidence.

My Mum manages my merchandise store, and we use part of our house as a sort of 'stockroom', and manage all of the distribution from there. Back in the day, when people did visit me, my mum would stand outside the front door handing out old, or misprinted merchandise to passing fans, much to their delight. My Mum is, and always has been, my biggest fan – people always ask me what my Mum thinks of what I do, and I always laugh... Most Mum's are over-the-top worried about what their kids get up to, but mine is a bigger fan than every single kid who stood outside my house back in the day, or who came to meet-and-greets, or bought posters and even this book!

Anyway – One evening, Lee and I were sat in his van outside my house, just chilling and spending the evening hanging out. We took some photos and videos on social media for our stories, nothing in particular, as I said, we were just hanging out.

For whatever reason, we came out of the van which was parked on the curb of my residential street. It must have been around three in the morning. Not many people were parked around the area, most people brought the cars onto their driveway or garage, and so the van looked stood-out on the empty, eerily quiet road.

"Mate!" Lee called me over. He was stood at the front of the van, having stopped in his tracks whilst walking around to get in on the road-side door. "Take a look at this!"

I walked back around the far side of the van and immediately noticed Lee's confused look.

"What?" I queried, and he nodded his head towards the wiper blade of my car. Our two confused faces must have been an entertaining sight, as we both stared at a pink and blue, rolled-up betting slip, underneath my left wiper blade.

Lee picked it up. As he lifted the paper, it unfurled, and two objects dropped onto the hood of the van. Our confusion only grew, and developed into shock when we saw what appeared to be two red and gold shotgun casings lying on the front of Lee's van.

"What the fuck..." I stammered, looking at Lee, who had a shocked smile on his face.

"Did you do this?" He asked, trying to find an explanation for the shock and confusion we both were feeling.

Again, we've pissed *a lot* of people off, even in the earlier days, and so it was only a matter of time before the "Infamous YouTube Pranksters" became the victim of a prank or two by a member of the public.

I picked one up to inspect. It was heavier than I anticipated, not *heavy*, but I'd never held a shotgun cartridge before. I turned it over so the flat gold-looking edge was facing up at me, revealing the word "LEE." engraved into it, in large intimidating letters.

"Fucking fuck what the fuck!" I picked up the second shell, and saw exactly I expected, but feared I would see...

"ALLY."

"Man, this isn't funny, for real!" I turned to Lee, desperately hoping he was pranking me, as my knees went numb. By this point Lee had seen his name on the first shell, and looked equally as confused and slightly terrified.

We locked the van and went straight inside after rolling the shells back in the betting-slip.

The police were called, but knowing who we were, they didn't take our concerns particularly seriously. They took photos, and that was the last we ever heard about the whole affair.

My mind tells me it was a fan playing a prank on us, but my gut tells me it was someone who we'd seriously crossed.

FREEFALLING

PART ½

Back in 2018, during the period of time where I was travelling as much as I could, having been to Dubai, Australia, and various locations out in Asia, I felt like I wanted to tackle something a bit more 'out-there', whilst on my travels. I normally would arrive at a location, see what there is to see, meet some cool people, make some memories doing some crazy climbs and such. But on this next trip, I wanted to learn something new.

I left for Los Angeles later in the year with the intention of earning my Skydiving License. I made my way to a small town an hour or two outside of Los Angeles called Perris, where the airport and skydiving school was situated.

This school was an insanely cool place, and came highly recommended. The day I arrived, Logan Paul, another controversial YouTuber and Hollywood actor, had graduated his course; I met some other creators, including Russia's *Vitaly*, and even Tom Cruise and James Corden had been there only days prior for some filming. It was a mad place.

The license I was going for was called the 'A License', which would make me a qualified skydiver. For this, I would need to make twenty-two jumps from an aircraft.

When I arrived, I anticipated hopping straight into the plane, and getting going — That was the kind of feeling this school had, however this wasn't the case. For six hours, we were sat in a classroom, being taught all about the science behind the jumping. Learning everything from all about the gear we would be using, all the way to details of wind-vectors and velocities. One of the main things that they drill into you over and over again is the phrase:

"Look red. Peel. Pull… Look grey. Peel. Pull."

This was the 'Cut-Away' procedure, and is pretty self-explanatory. You'd locate and confirm the Red tag, peel it away, and pull on it, which would dramatically detach you from your main canopy. You then would do the same for the Grey tag, which would deploy your reserve. This procedure was repeated over and over again, throughout the entirety of our six hours, drilling it deep into our minds as we continued the program. We then were put into a small hall, where they had installed dummy skydiving equipment rigged to the ceiling. Over and over again we went over our cutaway procedures.

"Look Red. Peel. Pull. Look Grey. Peel. Pull" we said to each other over and over again as we practiced, dangling from the ceilings like babies in a bouncer.

After all of these lessons and practice, it was time for our first jump. We would be taken up by two instructors, but jump independently, being walked through the landing technique by means of walkie-talkies. I am used to being at heights, but not from jumping from them! It was an unusual feeling for me, looking down from a height and actually being somewhat scared.

The jump went smoothly, but my walkie-talkie was far too quiet, and I must have missed some valuable instruction, because upon landing, I skidded on my arse, bruising both my coccyx and my pride. I couldn't think about that though, because I had just had the most surreal, but exhilarating thrill of my entire life so far…

I had just jumped out of a plane flying at thirteen-thousand feet in the sky, and landed safely, on my own. It felt very surreal. From that moment, I'd fallen in love, yet again, with something exhilarating, and could not wait to complete the course.

Jumping forwards to my seventeenth solo-jump, I was now quite confident with the entire process, and it felt much more like clockwork now, from getting into our kit, into the plane, out of the plane, and back on the ground.

We were over our drop-site, and well over ten-thousand feet. The door swung open, and we got ready to bail. I leapt out. As I was freefalling, I made a note to remember the feeling, as I was now in the latter stages of the training, and wouldn't have many more of these jumps before it was all over too soon!

"Yeah baby!" I passed five-thousand feet, the warm air smashing into my grinning face.

I pulled my chute and immediately entered a vicious spin to my right. My right-side toggle was stuck, and something was wrong. I was spinning faster now, and began to panic. I was dizzy, and now scared in a completely different way to the fear I felt on the edge of the plane before my first jump. I was scared for my life.

You don't have much time in a freefall to make decisions. In a matter of seconds, you'll be nothing more than a stain on the ground if you don't react quickly and correctly.

2,500 feet. This was the altitude we needed to have made our decisions by, as the parachute took around one-thousand feet to fully deploy. The wounded chute had slowed me down, but I was still plummeting towards the ground at break-neck speeds. Still spinning, and still dizzy, I knew I needed to act fast.

"Look red!" I firmly told myself, reaching around to find the red tag.

"Peel! Pull!" I pulled the tag and immediately reentered a freefall as the main canopy detached from my harness, the sudden unexpected acceleration taking my breath away.

"Look grey!" I shouted, and followed the same procedure to deploy the reserve parachute. Closing my eyes, and holding my breath as I pulled the tag. Within no more than two seconds, I was under the reserve, and slowing down in a controlled manner. The spinning had stopped, but my heart kept beating as hard and fast as I'd ever felt before. I screamed with heavy mix of joy and relief.

We had signed a waiver before we began the training, that any cutaway which we needed to do, we would be charged the full cost of $3000 to replace and repack the equipment. As I dangled from my reserve, watching my main canopy floating away... $3000 drifting away from me in the wind, and I could not have cared less! In this moment, it proved to me that when it comes to life and death, money means nothing. The value of your health, life, and happiness, is far greater than all of the money in the world.

The feeling of landing after that whole ordeal, was now *the most* exhilarated I've ever felt. I've been told that cheating death is often the most exciting feeling you never want to have, but when you do end up in a situation like the one I found myself in, thousands of feet in the air, it's incredibly rewarding when you do the right thing, and get yourself out of it intact.

I think it's important, when something scary or unnerving happens to you whilst doing something new, that you get straight up and back into it. In my opinion, that's the best way of beating a fear, before it even becomes a *fear*. So that's exactly what I did — Got straight back in that plane, and did my next jump.

I never was charged the $3000 fee, as the crew had managed to track down the canopy, which landed a few miles away. I covered the cost of some of the straps and rings that would need replacing, and a bit extra for their troubles, which totaled around five-hundred dollars, which I still say was the best money I've ever spent.

FREEFALLING

PART 2/2

Thankfully, my experience with skydiving was the only 'close call' I've had related to being at heights. I went on to finish the qualification in America, and have been lucky enough to be able to do plenty more jumps all over the place, and not just out of a plane...

Early in 2020, I started a new hobby which you may have noticed. Starting small, me and a few friends, some of who had some experience in this area, began cliff-jumping in various places in the UK. I soon found that this new activity was something I could become really hooked on, and it was, again, born out of an attempt to beat a fear I had developed from an occasion some time previously, whilst making a video.

One of my more popular videos involves myself and my friends sneaking into a leisure center, with a big diving pool, and boards of various heights. In the video, I climb up to the top of the ladder, get to the edge, but quickly back-away, and climb back down – Much to the ridicule and jeers of my enthusiastic and disappointed friends, as well as some people in the comments of the video. There was a reason for my changing of mind, however, that I never properly addressed. In 2018, soon after my return from LA, we had done a similar thing in a different pool-facility, where a very good mate of mine ran to the ten-meter diving board and leapt-off into the pool below. What he wasn't aware of, however, was that the pool had the ability to adjust its depth, dependent on what activity was being performed at that moment. Overnight, the facility had brought the pool to its *minimum* possible depth of less than five feet. After impacting the water, his legs smashed into the floor of the pool, seriously injuring his knees and spine.

As I reached the top of the diving board, I froze. My mind flashed back to this day, and knew that it would not be worth risking my life, if a similar situation had occurred.

I'm proud that I didn't jump in that day, however I was acutely aware that my cautiousness was quickly developing into a phobia, and I wanted to defeat it.

My addiction to adrenaline has become more thirsty over the years, and I no longer get the same buzz I once got from things like climbing cranes, or flipping on rooftops, so this new hobby was the perfect way to find, once again, the adrenaline buzz I needed, whilst beating my fear.

We would travel around, and find waterfalls, or small cliffs to jump off into water. It was something completely new to me, and frankly scared the hell out of me! It felt like I was at the very beginning of my whole story of starting to learn parkour again.

This really helped me think about where I want my career to go. I've known for a while that I want to 'mellow-out' my content and public appearance. I want to move away from controversy, and into a position where

I can use my platform to show off the lifestyle I want to live: Having fun, making memories, and not taking myself so seriously, as well as inspiring others in any way I can.

With cliff-jumping, for me, there was and still is so much progression to be had. We visited waterfalls not far from Glasgow, and met some other guys who had jumped there before. When we jump normally, we hop in the water beforehand and swim down to check if the depth of the water is suitable for the jump we are attempting. However, on this occasion, the water was flowing too fast to carry out this vital check, which I always made sure was done before we ever attempt a jump from height. The guys we were accompanied with, however, had jumped here many times, and showed their photos and videos of the depth of the water, and their previous jumps at this location. We inspected from the surface, and decided to go for it.

This jump was over ten meters (45 feet), and would be the tallest height I have ever jumped from. I stood on the edge, and before jumping, my mind flashed back to Dylan at the top of the 10m diving board. We had done our due diligence, but was it enough? I jumped in, safely completing the tallest jump to date.

Now, several months later, my legs still shake and wobble when I'm stood at the top of a jumping spot. I'm quite calm at the edge of a 300ft building, when it comes to jumping – that's a different story. I've never since gone without a depth-check, and will never neglect safety in exchange for adrenaline or entertainment. That said, the thrill of leaping off bridges into the icy rivers of north Wales, or the fast-flowing waterfall pools of the peak-district, gives me an adrenaline-fix that I used to feel, way back in the day, climbing cranes and building sites… and I piss a lot less people off!

I've fallen in love with the hobby, and would recommend it to anyone. So long as they are by professionals, and know the risks involved. You will most certainly hurt yourself. I've slapped my balls onto the water a fair few times, and emerged with teary eyes, but the experience you feel is unbeatable.

IT'S A CYCLE

As I'm sure is clear at this point into this book, that I've gotten to a point where I am lucky-enough to have achieved so much of what I've always wanted to have achieved… Skydiving, world-travelling, even scuba-diving, and all of this is amazing. However, in recent history, I've been desperate to set goals and achievements based on doing more good, and positive things. I'm lucky I have the following I do, on YouTube, as well as social media, and I really wanted to do something good with this following.

I follow a musician online called John Joseph, who, in my opinion, he has one of the most inspiring life stories I've heard, and is famously an extremely positive person. He always says:

"Being a service to others, is the best thing you can ever do"

He is always out creating good in the world, and doing his best to make people happy. He regularly completes 'Ironman' challenges, which if you aren't aware, consists of a 2.6-mile swim, followed by a 112-mile bike ride, and *then* a full marathon, all back to back! Not only does he train and compete in these events, something which is noteworthy in itself, but he always dedicates them to raising money for charities, individuals, or other good causes; He's seen often in New York cooking up feasts for the homeless population, and I've always considered him just an all-round 'badass' human being, with an incredible story, and even more incredible heart.

I was on a plane out to Thailand in early 2020, and read his book, in full, titled "The PMA Effect". It made me think a lot, about how over the last seven years or so of my life, I've been non-stop grinding to make *my life* awesome. I've worked my arse off to get to where I am now, as I write these words. I've wanted to live a fantastically fun life and do epic things - creating mad memories - but upon deep thought and review, I found mine to be quite a selfish viewpoint. Although my *intentions* weren't, and have never been selfish, it's always, all about me.

I'm infinitely far from being a perfect person, but I have always tried to be a *good* person. If I can help somebody out, I will. I started giving more to charity; I'd stop on the street and buy a hot meal for someone who didn't have a place to go, and did my best to be a more selfless person – But it wasn't enough. I thought to myself that I could be doing *more*. I have millions of followers online, and have a huge platform that I've built up for years and years, but ultimately, it's all been for my own selfish gain. With my newfound clarity, I felt the need to do better things, and be better with this platform I've worked so hard to achieve.

I have decided that in the future, I would love to set up an animal charity, having been an animal-lover for my entire life. Much sooner though, I plan on working to help provide sanctuary and shelter for homeless people, in my local city and beyond. Sadly, having the idea is the easy part, and we're still a year away from delivering on the start of these projects, which leaves me still feeling like I haven't been enough of a service to others.

I saw a Tweet in which I had been mentioned, in late-June 2020, with a request for me to help by sharing it. The tweet linked to a story called *'Save our Stan'*, about a two-year-old boy from Carlisle, with an extremely rare case of leukemia. He had already undertaken multiple bone marrow transplants, and a variety of serious surgeries, and had been in and out of hospital since he was just six-teen-months old. In June of 2020, the NHS told Stan's parents that there was no more treatment they would be able to offer him, meaning sadly, little Stan would be unlikely to survive his illness.

Stan's family found a light at the end of the tunnel, when they were told about a new treatment which had proved successful on quite a number of other children in Stan's position. The cost was £500,000, and Stan and his parents would need to move to Singapore to undertake this treatment. Stan's family couldn't afford this, and if I could myself, I certainly would have paid for the treatment. — But that's not the kind of money I have either. They had turned to fundraising, and were already quite close to the target, but it has slowed considerably, and time was running out for Stan. The story broke my heart. When I had finished reading, I sat in my car and cried my eyes out for Stan's family. I cannot imagine what it was like for them, going through this, and for Stan, who is just a young child. Now was an opportunity for me to use my platform for good.

I wanted to do something huge for Stan, that wouldn't be something I'd find easy. Stan's life, and the life of his family has been tougher than anything I could dream of tackling, but I wanted to push myself to the limit of what I could achieve.

I looked at my skills, and my physical ability, and for some reason, settled on doing something that fell into neither of these categories! I decided in mid-June to attempt to cycle, on my own, with no previous training, from Land's-End, the southernmost tip of mainland Britain, to John O'Groats, the northernmost tip – A total of one-thousand and ten miles. From the very moment I decided this, I knew it was incredibly naive of me to attempt this challenge for Stan, but in my mind, however far I would make it, I would give my absolute all to this attempt, and hopefully raise enough money to make a dent in the remaining funds that little Stan needed for his treatment.

The Sunday before I set off, I was running around town desperately trying to get my bike serviced. My tires hadn't been changed in years, the gears were a little dodgy, and overall it just needed some TLC. I purchased a GPS device, so I'd be able to view my distances, speed, and various other statistics I may need throughout my journey. I stocked up on gels, purchased the cheapest sleeping-bag I could find... But the end of the day was fast approaching, and I still hadn't been able to replace my worn-out tires. I had given up, and decided I'd have to do without, despite the bike-store mechanic telling me they would not make fifty-miles without problems.

In what some may call, true Ally Law fashion, I ignored the professional advice, and went on my way!

I stayed the night at my friend Aaron's home in a town called *Turo*, which is about a forty-five-minute drive from

Land's End. I managed to sneak-in around three hours of sleep, before setting off to my journey's starting point.

I'd never actually visited Land's End, so it was quite a cool thing to tick off my bucket list, but I didn't have much time to take in the scenery before I got on my bike, and began my attempt at an over one-thousand-mile journey, with no preparation, and no professional training. On Friday, I was sat on my bed, in my boxers, scrolling endlessly through social-media, stuffing myself with junk-food, and now here I was, on my saddle, about to embark on the most intense challenge I may ever experience.

I felt an overwhelming sense of pride in myself, which you may say is selfish, but I was happy that I was helping young Stan, and pushing myself to my limits to do so, in fact, I had already raised over £8000 before I even got on my bike! That was an insane feeling, and I knew I had to do my very best, no matter how far I made it!

I could only take the bare essentials, and I didn't own a backpack! I had to use one of my duffel-bags with my branding on, and chucked all of the things I would need inside. Food, cameras, sleeping bag. I had to ditch most of the things I intended on bringing in my car, but it didn't matter. I wore the duffel-bag like a rucksack, over my shoulders, which I can now happily tell any reader, that this is absolutely not the intention of the design!

The first day, I was filled with excitement and adrenaline, I went for eleven hours. However, towards the end of the day, I imagine the handles which I had adopted as makeshift shoulder-straps were digging into my armpit a little too tight, as my arm started to get more and more numb. It got to the point where I could barely send a text on my phone, let alone change gears.

I noticed this was a real problem, and powered through the last of the 101 miles that evening, before calling it a day. I was very surprised I had made it this far, but after defeating the brutal hills of Cornwall, the majority of the ride was quite manageable.

Day two. I set off strong, but the hills continued to get worse and worse. I remember saying to myself for what felt like hours:

"It's just hill after hill, after hill, after hill!"

To add insult to injury, it was raining - heavily! The rain was soaking me through, and the hills taking their toll on my knee. I don't think I have ever felt as much pain as I did in my knee by the end of that second day. I could only manage 77 miles, and passing through Taunton, I considered calling it a day, and getting up early to push through, but I didn't want to stop there. I wanted to finish my target of 100 miles a day, but my knee was giving me a lot of pain, and I told myself that with some rest, I'd be able to carry on the following day with a lot more energy. I was scrolling through Instagram messages, and accidently clicked onto a message request from a guy named Luke. Luke offered to let me crash for the night at his home... *In Taunton!*

I considered myself incredibly lucky, and accepted his generous invite.

As it turns out to both of our surprise, Luke and I had mutual friends. We ordered a mammoth amount of food from a local takeaway. My tracker telling me I burned somewhere in the region of seven-thousand calories that day alone... I did not feel guilty in the slightest for stuffing my face!

This is where life is funny, I find it hard to believe there isn't something, or someone out there watching over me sometimes. Some experiences I have had where things seem to just work out; or I just meet somebody or something happens that is so bizarrely coincidental it's almost unexplainable. Luke and I are sat in his living room talking to a friend of his called Matt, who is *another* person I've met before! I met him during a meet-up I organised in Leicester Square, 2018. During our conversation, he revealed was close to some more internet urban-explorers called *Exploring with Fighters*. It just so happened that they were doing a livestream that evening. After only some brief discussion, I was hopping on to join them on their livestream, where they allowed me to promote the charity ride I was attempting. They were kind enough to dedicate the entire stream to the ride, and Stan, and raised a whopping *two-thousand* pounds, and all in less than a few hours! I was, and still am, immensely grateful for this.

I managed to rest-up, take a much-needed shower, eat some more, and head to sleep, but not before massaging the back of my knee what must have been around two hours.

I woke up feeling fresh, surprisingly, resolving to myself that it was the right thing to have done to stop for the night. I'm just grateful that someone or something was watching over me that day to make me coincidently click on that message from Luke. He is a top guy, and I hope looking back that I told him just how grateful I was.

I was going to make sure I made up for the miles I had lost out on yesterday, but was already mentally preparing for the hills to get the better of me again. Whilst leaving Taunton, and cycling through Somerset, I was pleasantly surprised: The sun was out, and the sky was beautifully clear. I enjoyed stunning views of nature surrounding the country lanes which formed most of my route. It was a stark contrast to the previous two days!

I managed to push through to 130 miles on the third day, which ended me near Worcester. I fully intended to sleep outdoors, with my hammock and sleeping bag, for the entirety of this journey, but over the years of travelling, interacting with, and meeting new people, it was a pleasant realisation that I seemed to have friends dotted all over the country. A blessing for the situation I was in.

Naomi, a good friend of mine who've I've known for years, was, at the time, living full time in her campervan. On this day, she was only about forty-five minutes away from me, and kindly offered to come and cook me a vegan-feast and hang out for the night. I hadn't seen her in so long, as she had been out in South America, travelling and exploring. As long as I've known her, I've always said she's probably the most amazing girl, with the loveliest personality of anyone I've ever met. We spent the evening swimming in this ice-cold lake, and relaxing after a long day. She helped me gather some supplies for the days ahead, including some heat spray for my leg. We both slept in the van, and before I knew it, it was 07:00AM, and I was off again. Today, I was determined to make it all the way to Manchester.

I checked the fundraising page, as I did every hour religiously. We had raised a touch under twenty-thousand pounds! This motivated me. We were two thirds of my goal of £30,000, and I felt inspired, emotional, and desperate to get going, and make it as far as I possibly could for Stan. I was pushing my body to its limit, and it felt so good to be bringing so much awareness to Stan's cause.

I had done one-hundred and one miles now, and was about twenty-two away from Manchester. It was now getting late though, and I was just trying to rush ahead to get there before dark, maintaining a good pace. It was a pretty grueling, but uneventful day, my knee tendons began to hurt again at roughly the seventy-mile point, which I was just pushing through. I put on some heat cream, and some head pads on my knees (which I later learned was one of the worst things I could have done!), and just carried on pushing through naively…

I had a great attitude through the one-hundred-mile point, and was out of the saddle, powering my legs to pedal me up a huge hill. I was driving with my feet on the pedals when all of a sudden, I felt like something tore, and pinged in the back of my achilles, making me cringe, before the new, most horrendous pain rushed over my leg. I pulled off the road and lay down on the grass, sobbing in pain. I felt it in my heart at this moment, that any further miles I was able to clock would be a blessing, but that my journey may soon be coming to an end. I lay there for half an hour, rubbing my leg, and wincing at the slightest pressure I put on my muscles.

I got on the bike. It was forecasted to rain buckets that night, and I was in the middle of nowhere, with no shelter. Lined up for me, was a bed at my friend, Simon's house who lived in Manchester…I *had* to make it to Manchester.

After several painful failed attempts, I found that if I pedaled with the center of my foot, without moving my toes, or putting pressure on other areas, I could just about manage to keep a reasonable pace, with minimal pain to my ankle, and only a small amount of discomfort to my knee… I kept reminding myself that I could do nothing about the pain right now, but *suffering* is a choice, and I wasn't going to suffer.

I made it to Manchester, but cycling the remaining twenty-one miles took its toll on my knee. I was encouraged by the many messages and comments of support I had received, as well as the rising total of contributions to Stan's cause. A fan had spotted me, and pulled his car over to greet me, and give me words of support. He also gave me a massage gun, hoodie, and some vegan snacks. This amazing stranger reminded me so much of John Joseph, whose kindness and selflessness had inspired me to be where I was in this very moment. He didn't want a shout-out; to be named, nor to be on my social-media, or any videos receiving thanks or praise, he just wanted to lend a hand. People tell me all the time that I inspire them, but people like this stranger are the ones who inspire me. People who go out to put good in the world. He offered to take me the last nine miles of that leg, and that he wouldn't tell a soul… but of course, I had to refuse.

In hindsight, that may have been the best thing to do for my body – Because when I arrived at Simon's in Manchester, my lower leg felt as if it could have dropped out of its joint at any moment! Simon invited his chiropractor friend over for the evening, who spent some time on me, clicking and cracking me back into shape! It felt good, but sadly wasn't helping my leg enough.

I rested until morning and then said goodbye, once again; my naivety and desperation to complete as much as I could of this seemingly impossible mission, getting the better of me! I made it less than two-miles, before collapsing in pure agony, once again. This wasn't going to happen for me today.

I went back to Simon's and spent the day resting, icing my leg, and desperately wanting my leg to magically heal so I could push forwards. Twenty-four hours passed, and I still could barely walk. On the third day at Simon's, he took me to a bike store to attempt to purchase some proper cycling shoes, something I definitely should have done before setting off! Who knows, if I had been more prepared and bought some shoes back in Southampton, before my journey began, I would have probably been in Scotland by now!

Another day went past, and nothing had improved. In fact, I think the situation had even gotten worse. I had never been in this much pain or even really had any significant sporting injuries. I messaged my friend Chase, another very well-known freerunner, who had *torn* his achilles last year. He made clear to me that it's not something you want to tear. He needed a twelve-month recovery period, and couldn't walk for the best part of a year. I also had a few doctors messaging me on Instagram, telling me I likely had a very small tear, or rupture, or *achilles tendonitis*, and if I were to keep pushing, I was going to cause serious damage that could very well last my entire life.

On the third or fourth day, after having first stopped at Simon's, I had cycled all of two miles, and had to make a hard choice. I was under a motorway bridge in Manchester, with my bike, hiding from the rain, when I decided I needed to throw in the towel.

Although I had told myself I would cycle as far as I physically could for this cause, I still felt like I had failed. But as time goes on, I realise that John O'Groats or not, I had pushed myself to my absolute, clearly defined *limit*, in pursuit of helping Stan and his family.

We raised a little over twenty-four thousand pounds when I brought an end to my cycle – Roughly 5% of the total the family needed. I keep in touch with the family, who thankfully reached their fundraising target. Stan's Dad, Lee, kindly got in touch with me a month or so later.

They were heading to Singapore, and Stan will receive his treatment.

I've cried so much for Stan and his family, and finally I was crying tears of joy and elation. I wasn't single-handedly responsible for the success of Stan's fundraising efforts, but I did my best, and many others did too, and all together, we've got Stan a fighting chance.

Cycling for Stan.

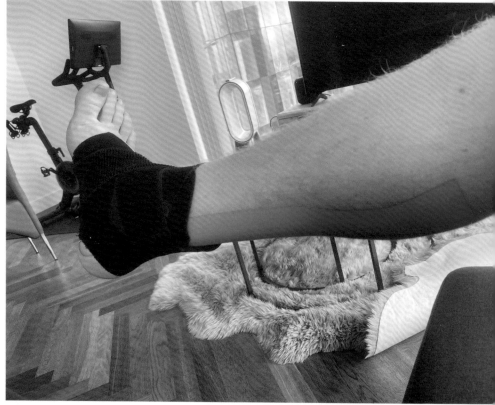

TAKE NO L

People think I have the dream life, but there have been plenty of occasions where I've felt miserable, uninspired, or directionless.

Late 2019 was one of those times. I felt lost. It felt like everybody was looking at this life I was living, being entertained, and I struggled to find any motivation for anything in my life. I felt goalless, like I, on paper, had achieved everything I ever wanted, and had nothing left to do. It's a bad way of treating ambition in life, but my mind was constantly telling me that I no longer had any purpose. Its damaging to treat yourself like that, and I knew it, but I felt like I was falling into a spiral of self-doubt and depression. I didn't *feel* depressed, but every day was becoming a struggle, to be motivated to do everything I once considered normal.

I started eating like shit. I fell into old habits once again. I gained weight, and felt myself spiraling further. I was aware that this wasn't good. I'd been told by people who suffered from depression for many years, who I either know personally, or who found me through my videos, that it all starts with a spiraling feeling. I had lost almost all my inspiration, and my videos, and more importantly, my mental health was suffering. I needed something to pull me out.

I was sat on the sofa in early September, binge eating junk-food, as I was doing more and more often, when I received a phone call with an offer for me to take part in a 'YouTuber' MMA fight in December. Tickets would be sold to fans of both the 'fighters', and that would be a great opportunity to do something a bit more out of the box for me. I took a chance, and accepted the offer.

Most people know that this story ends with me losing a close-fight with a creator called Joe Henderson, but behind the scenes, this story is my story of how I pulled myself from a personal, physical, and emotional rut, which I had spiraled into in previous months.

I started working out, and committing myself to getting in shape. Every morning of every day I was in the gym, even during travels to Dubai with my mates later in the year, I was up before the sun rose, busting-out a killer workout before everyone woke up, and a day of filming and exploring could begin. Back in the UK, I enlisted the help of a former MMA fighter and good friend of mine named Owen Gayle, to help me train. For five or six hours a day, I was in a martial-arts gymnasium, training non-stop. I finally felt like I was pulling myself out of my rut. I was getting fitter, and snapped back into my much healthier habits. I cut processed food, and strictly stuck to a vegan diet, something which I've continued to this day.

Every day, as a part of my general fitness plan, I would run for two minutes in the gym, maintaining a high-heart-rate; rest for one minute, and then start again. Ten, fifteen, or twenty times. It would kill me, but every day I could see my own improvement, which was a hugely significant motivator for me.

December came, and I lost the fight, but it wasn't about that for me. I had an amazing experience, and a lot of fun. I got fit, and into healthy habits I hope to stick to for the rest of my life. But most importantly, it taught me that sometimes, all you need is something to pour your heart into, to give you a much greater sense of fulfilment.

For me, the mind and body has an unbelievably strong link. When you push your body to its limits, your mind can suffer, and when your mind feels like it is at its limit, your body, and thusly your heath, will suffer. I'm incredibly privileged to have been able to pull myself out of various spirals of poor mental health throughout my short time on this planet, as I'm aware so many others have not been this lucky.

I'm grateful to hear from fans of the videos that I have helped *them*, or pulled *them* out of a rut. I never really know how to feel about this, other than thankful that I have the platform which I do, to be able to entertain these people in such a way that it really, really helps them. I think we idolize celebrities and YouTube creators too much, but I also think that some people get a real sense of connection to someone's life, or adventures, whilst watching their videos, allowing them an escape from their problems, even just for ten minutes out of a day. For me, that's an incredibly satisfying thing to provide someone who needs it.

After losing the fight, whenever I feel like I could start spiraling, or that I have no more goals left to strive towards, I remind myself of my biggest goal, one which I don't think I could 'complete', and that is to entertain people, who want to be entertained, and help people who

I have the power to help. To do good, and to be good to others.

THE HOMELESS YOUTUBER'S GUIDE TO A HAPPY LIFE

As I write this, I'm living in a van, travelling around the UK, with little to no money, having the time of my life. I've had the opportunity to travel the world, be rich and very poor, but I've found that the happiest I've been, is all since I started following some simple rules for life.

I appreciate I'm woefully underqualified to give life-advice, but as I look back over recent history, and how much my happiness has improved as time goes on, and I feel like I should use my platform to share any and all happiness with everyone I can.

I'm twenty-three years old, but have been through a fair amount for my age I think. I've striven to make up for the years I lost as a young teen, in my battle with mental health and addiction, when my family seemed to be falling apart. I've learned to make the most out of every second; I've learned to be careful, diligent and put my health and wellbeing, and that of my close friends and family, above all.

People think I'm a reckless idiot, and I don't blame them. It certainly looks that way, but I don't want to look back on a life of sitting in an office, collecting a paycheck, and going on holiday once a year, living for the weekends. I want to live a life full of adventure, as I think everybody should.

For me, the adventure of scaling buildings in the dead of night; or climbing bridges with police sirens wailing one-hundred feet below, are coming to an end. My new adventure is about bettering myself, and putting good into the world; It's about pursuing not just adrenaline, but the thrill of exploring new things, learning skills, and taking leaps of faith. Standing on the edge, and looking over, at the ground below, without trembling, metaphorically speaking, of course...

I'm looking to start a business, completely independent of my name and web-personality, with the aim to provide fresh and clean juices to people on subscription; I'm working with more charities, and even in the process of setting up my own. Focusing on homelessness in my hometown and beyond.

I want to deliver to my followers, content that is exciting, action and adrenaline packed, whilst emphasizing more on less controversial activities travelling around the UK, and the world. Often, when most people outside of my immediate fan base hear my name, they say:

"Reckless criminal."

"Nuisance!"

In itself, this doesn't bother me, as being the person I am and doing what I do has put me in a position today with a platform that I can use for good.

Robin Hood was legendary for being kind; he stole from the rich and gave to the poor. I don't steal from anybody, but from building a career on what people happily call me criminal for doing. I can strive to *give* to the people who need it, as I've always tried to do, through my content, and now, going into the future, through charity, and more.

As my Granddad said: "It's better to try and fail, than to always wonder 'what if?'"

Stop Caring About What People Think.

People will always have opinions about what you do, but it's important to remember that these opinions are usually based on their already existing beliefs about you, and these beliefs are, in turn, based on what they would do instead.

Who cares what they would do? If something brings you joy and excitement, don't let what you think someone thinks about you, stop you.

Be Confident.

It's easier said than done. But if you know me, you know I believe that you can do anything with a bit of confidence. I've proved this time and again through what I do, but even in everyday life, talking and acting with confidence will make you feel more confident – Use this to chase what you want. You'll find that this is a snowball effect: The more confident you act, the more confident you feel!

> **"With a High-Viz & Confidence, You Can Do Anything!"**

Be Nice.

People who know little about me, often assume I'm un-caring or delinquent in my personality, however, I really value kindness and person-to-person respect. It's easy to brighten someone's day by just smiling, chatting, and showing interest in someone's day — it a friend, or even just a stranger at a shop.

Don't Be Afraid.

So many of my stunts and adventures have come about from my desire to conquer my fears. This doesn't mean I am of the opinion that you should go and jump off a bridge, or climb a skyscraper, all I mean is that fear should never be the reason you aren't doing something. Whether it's the fear of failure, or the fear of looking silly, or any other fear, it should never be a reason.

I'm not telling you to do dangerous things… as not doing something because it's dangerous isn't being afraid; it's being *sensible!*

Get out of your comfort-zone. Good things come to those that do.

Seize Every Opportunity

Every bit of bad news is a door opening. Every bump in the road is a ramp you can use to get something you want, or somewhere you want to be.

I left school with nothing. I had no skills, and no qualifications. I've made a career out of having fun, learning skills, and a little bit of luck. I've seized every opportunity I could to improve myself, who I am, and my career.

> **"We Don't Take L's!"**

Be Grateful

I'll keep this one short. Gratitude is underrated. Reminding myself every day what it is exactly that I'm grateful for, has made me a much happier and more fulfilled man. Be grateful for something every day.